I want to be like Jesus

MARYBETH HAGEMAN

ILLUSTRATED BY
REG SANDLAND

AUGSBURG ● MINNEAPOLIS

To Betsy, Sally, and Natalie
who help me see God with new eyes

Daddy reads me stories from the Bible. He tells me Jesus was just my size long ago. Jesus must have sat on Joseph's lap and heard stories, too. I want to be like Jesus.

People came to hear Jesus speak. They got hungry. Jesus and his helpers gave them bread and fish to eat.

Mommy gave me two cookies. When Susan came to play, I gave one to her. I want to share like Jesus.

A father brought his sick little boy to Jesus.
Jesus made the boy well so he could run and play.
The little boy and his father were happy.

Andy hurt his leg and had to stay in bed for a long time. I couldn't make him well, but I drew him a funny picture. Andy laughed. I want to make friends happy like Jesus.

Some fishermen couldn't catch any fish. Every time they pulled in their net, it was empty. Jesus told them where to fish. The fishermen fished where Jesus told them, and their net was filled with fish.

Jessica built a house out of blocks. It took her a long time. Then it fell over, and she started to cry. I said, "Don't cry, Jessica. I'll help you build another house." I want to be a helper like Jesus.

When Jesus was a boy, he liked to go to the temple. One time Mary and Joseph couldn't find him. They looked in the temple. Jesus was there, talking about God.

I go to church to hear about God and to sing happy songs. I like to go to church like Jesus.

Jesus walked from town to town, telling all the
people how much God loved them.

I told Daniel about God, and he came to Sunday school with me. Daniel had fun and wants to learn more. It's fun to tell others about God, like Jesus did.

Jesus liked to talk to God. He prayed, "Our Father in heaven. . . ."

I like to talk to God, too—just like Jesus. I fold my hands and squeeze my eyes shut. I pray, "Thank you for my friends, for Mommy and Daddy, for cookies to eat, and most of all, for Jesus."

It makes me happy to be like Jesus.

"Blessed are all . . . who walk in his ways."
—Psalm 128:1